STAR MATHS PUZZLES & PROBLEMS

A fresh approach to using and applying maths

TERMS AND CONDITIONS

IMPORTANT - PERMITTED USE AND WARNINGS - READ CAREFULLY BEFORE USING

This CD-ROM has been tested for viruses at all stages of its production. However, we recommend that you run virus-checking software on your computer systems at all times. Scholastic Ltd cannot accept any responsibility for any loss, disruption or damage to your data or your computer system that may occur as a result of using either the CD-ROM or the data held on it.

IF YOU ACCEPT THE ABOVE CONDITIONS YOU MAY PROCEED TO USE THE CD-ROM.

Minimum specification:
- PC or Mac with a CD-ROM drive and at least 128 Mb RAM
- Recommended screen resolution: 1280 × 1024 pixels. (See CD help notes for details.)
- Facilities for printing

PC:
- Windows 98SE or above
- Recommended minimum processor speed: 600 MHz

Mac:
- Mac OSX1. or above
- Recommended minimum processor speed: 500 MHz

For all technical support queries, please phone Scholastic Customer Services on 0845 6039091.

Julie Cogill and Anthony David

Authors
Julie Cogill and Anthony David

Development Editor
Niamh O'Carroll

Editor
Nicola Morgan

Assistant Editor
Margaret Eaton

Illustrations
Pages 12-20, 22-26 & 28-31 © Wizzmedia

Pages 6-9, 21, 34-42 & 47 © Janice Bowles, originally published in *Targeting Maths Problem Solving Level 1* (Pascal Press, 2007)

Page 6 'Use a tally' icon, page 8 'Estimation' icon, page 10 & page 38 'Balloons' © Scholastic Ltd

Series Designer
Joy Monkhouse

Designer
Melissa Leeke

CD-ROM design and development in association with Wizzmedia

Designed using Adobe CS

Published by Scholastic Ltd
Villiers House, Clarendon Avenue,
Leamington Spa, Warwickshire CV32 5PR
www.scholastic.co.uk

Printed by Tien Wah, Singapore
1 2 3 4 5 6 7 8 9   8 9 0 1 2 3 4 5 6 7

ISBN 978-1407-10032-6

ACKNOWLEDGEMENTS
Extracts from the Primary National Strategy's *Primary Framework for Mathematics* (2006) www.standards.dfes.gov.uk/primaryframework © Crown copyright. Reproduced under the terms of the Click Use Licence.

The approved SMART Software Accreditation logo is a trademark of SMART Technologies.

Every effort has been made to trace copyright holders for the works reproduced in this book, and the publishers apologise for any inadvertent omissions.

British Library Cataloguing-in-Publication Data
A catalogue record for this book is available from the British Library.

Introduction

Children need to learn how to solve problems by using and applying mathematics in a variety of contexts. However, when the *Framework for teaching mathematics from Reception to Year 6* was published in 1999, the focus was very much on number and calculations. The 1999 Framework has objectives under the broad heading of 'Solving problems', sub-divided into three sections:

- Making decisions
- Reasoning and generalising about numbers and shapes
- Problems involving 'real life', money or measures

At this point the National Curriculum gave much more attention to 'Using and applying mathematics', building it into all of the mathematics attainment targets. One of the principal aims of the renewed Primary Framework in 2006 therefore was to give greater attention to using and applying mathematics through the five themes of:

- Solving problems
- Representing
- Enquiring
- Reasoning
- Communicating

Star Maths Puzzles and Problems is designed to provide opportunities for children to use and apply mathematics in line with these themes and objectives. Each title reflects progression within the five themes by providing problems that encompass the full range of problem-solving processes and skills. The ten interactive problems on the CD-ROM will involve children in reasoning and predicting outcomes, in communicating their results, and in solving problems and developing lines of enquiry. Additionally, they provide opportunities for children to use problem-solving strategies to help them investigate and understand the mathematical content of each problem. What's more, the activities are engaging and challenging for all ability levels and most can be used flexibly either with the whole class on an interactive whiteboard or in small groups working at a computer.

About the book

Each book includes a set of teachers' notes linked to the interactive activities on the CD-ROM. A range of additional support is also provided, including an introduction to problem-solving strategies such as 'draw a diagram', an objectives grid, follow-up problems linked to the CD-ROM activities and a 'problems bank' designed to consolidate or assess children's grasp of each problem-solving strategy.

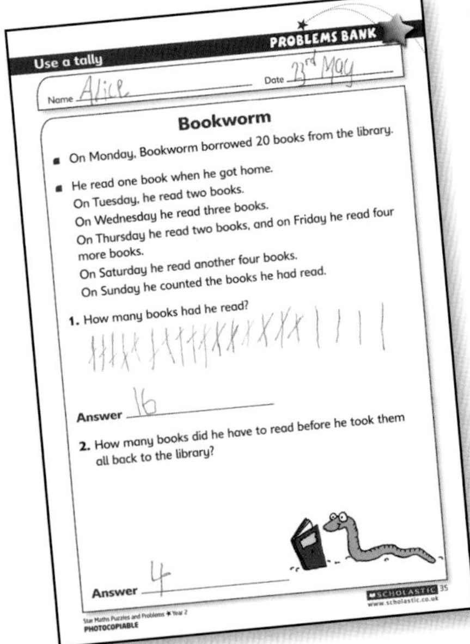

PROBLEMS BANK

Use a tally

Name Alice Date 23rd May

Bookworm

- On Monday, Bookworm borrowed 20 books from the library.
- He read one book when he got home.
  On Tuesday, he read two books.
  On Wednesday he read three books.
  On Thursday he read two books, and on Friday he read four more books.
  On Saturday he read another four books.
  On Sunday he counted the books he had read.

1. How many books had he read?

Answer 16

2. How many books did he have to read before he took them all back to the library?

Answer 4

Star Maths Puzzles and Problems ★ Year 2
PHOTOCOPIABLE

SCHOLASTIC 35
www.scholastic.co.uk

Strategies for using and applying

This book focuses on seven of the key strategies used in mathematical problem solving. Understanding these strategies will greatly assist children in making decisions about how to solve a problem, in organising and interpreting information and results and ultimately in finding solutions to problems. The strategies covered in this book include:

- Act it out
- Use a tally
- Draw a diagram
- Trial and improvement
- Estimation
- Look for patterns
- Logical reasoning

This section offers a rationale for each strategy, as well as issues to consider when children are starting to learn different strategies.

Teachers' notes

The teachers' notes cover the ten interactive activities on the CD-ROM. Each page of teachers' notes includes:

Learning objectives

Cover the strands and objectives of the renewed *Primary Framework for Mathematics* (2006) (using and applying objectives as well as objectives from other strands).

Problem-solving strategies

Suggestions for particular strategies to use to solve each CD-ROM problem.

Setting the scene

Setting the context of the problem and instructions for presenting the CD-ROM activity to the children.

Solving the problem

Notes on how to use a particular strategy to solve the CD-ROM problem.

Key questions

Probing questions to be used during the activity, sub-divided by the five themes of using and applying mathematics (see page 4 for further information).

Differentiation

Adapting the activity for more or less confident learners.

Follow up

Getting the children together to consolidate the learning, using practical activities and the related 'follow-up problems' activity sheets.

Problems bank

References to problems bank sheets (see below).

Annotations

At-a-glance instructions for using the CD-ROM activity.

Problems bank

For children to be able to find solutions in unfamiliar situations, they need to have experienced a wide variety of problems and puzzles and be able to call upon a bank of strategies with which to solve them. The 'problems bank' offers a range of problems designed to develop children's understanding of puzzles and problems and build up their use of strategies to solve them. The grid on pages 32–33 breaks down each problem by strategy or objective to help you to select appropriate problems.

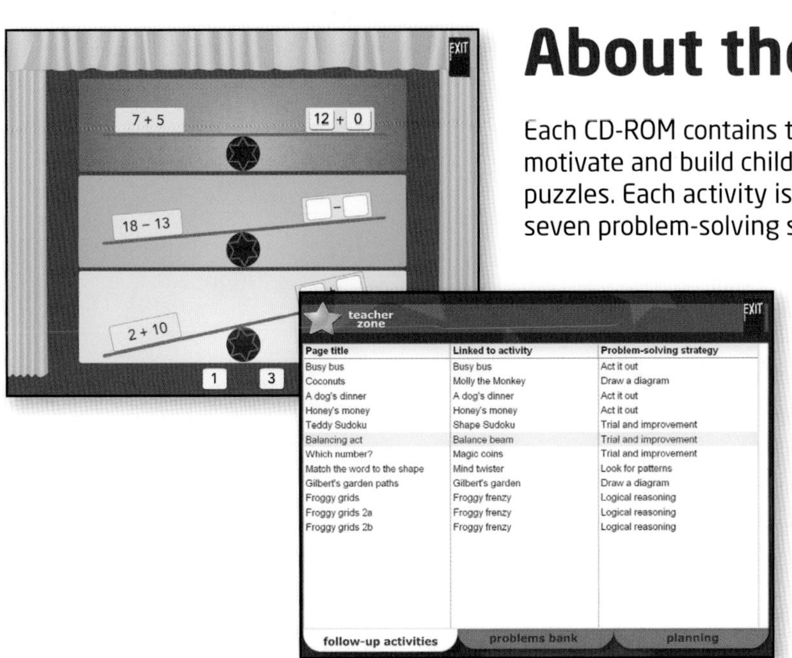

Page title	Linked to activity	Problem-solving strategy
Busy bus	Busy bus	Act it out
Coconuts	Molly the Monkey	Draw a diagram
A dog's dinner	A dog's dinner	Act it out
Honey's money	Honey's money	Act it out
Teddy Sudoku	Shape Sudoku	Trial and improvement
Balancing act	Balance beam	Trial and improvement
Which number?	Magic coins	Trial and improvement
Match the word to the shape	Mind twister	Look for patterns
Gilbert's garden paths	Gilbert's garden	Draw a diagram
Froggy grids	Froggy frenzy	Logical reasoning
Froggy grids 2a	Froggy frenzy	Logical reasoning
Froggy grids 2b	Froggy frenzy	Logical reasoning

About the CD-ROM

Each CD-ROM contains ten inspiring interactive activities designed to motivate and build children's confidence in solving maths problems and puzzles. Each activity is also designed to practise and reinforce one of the seven problem-solving strategies identified on pages 6-10. The problems are multi-faceted so that the children can return to them over and over again.

The CD-ROM also includes a Teacher zone containing editable objective grids, planning grids and printable versions of the follow-up problems and 'problems bank' activity sheets. Some additional 'problems bank' activities have also been supplied for further support and reinforcement.

Act it out

Rationale

The importance of the use of this strategy to help children understand mathematical concepts is well established. Using concrete materials provides a foundation of practical experience on which children can build abstract ideas. It encourages them to be inventive, aids concept and skill development and enhances understanding of processes. It helps clarify ideas, develops confidence and encourages independence. It is an effective strategy for those who have difficulty visualising a problem. Acting out a problem can greatly simplify finding solutions.

Teaching the strategy

Write a sample problem on the board, for example:

Mrs Muddle, the cook, is decorating eight cakes. She wants to put five cherries on top of each cake. How many cherries does Mrs Muddle need?

- Ask the children to read the problem. Ask: *What have you been asked to find? What information have you been given?*
- Explain that one way to solve this problem is to act out the problem using people or objects.
- Suggest: *We can use cups for the cakes and use counters for the cherries.* Line up eight cups for the children to see. Invite a child to put five counters in each 'cake' to represent the cherries.
- Say: *Let's count the cherries together!*
- Ask: *How many cherries does Mrs Muddle need?*
- Ask the children to suggest other objects that could be used to represent the cakes and the cherries.

Encourage the children to suggest other problems and discuss them as a class. Use the 'Busy bus', 'A dog's dinner' and 'Honey's money' activities on the CD-ROM and the problems-bank examples to develop understanding of this strategy.

Links to

Busy bus
pages 12-13

A dog's dinner
pages 16-17

Honey's money
pages 18-19

Use a tally

Rationale

Visualisations are necessary for children's understanding of mathematical concepts and relationships. Making a simple tally on paper is a systematic method of organising information that enables children to examine data and reach solutions more easily than they could by simply looking at unorganised numbers.

Teaching the strategy

Write a problem appropriate to your children's ages and mathematical knowledge on the board, for example:

I have twenty balloons. Six fly away. How many are left?

- Explain to the children that one way to solve the problem is to make a tally. They should just use a simple pencil stroke on a sheet of paper to represent objects.

- Demonstrate by drawing 20 strokes on the board and say: *These are the twenty balloons.*
- Cross out six and say: *These are the balloons that have flown away. We can see how many balloons are left. We count fourteen, so there are fourteen balloons left.*
- Ask the children how they can check to see if they are right. Show them how to count the strokes, saying: *We count one... fourteen, and then add the six that flew away. The answer is twenty, so we are correct.*
- Write on the board: 20 - 6 = 14.

Links to

Busy bus
pages 12-13

Use the 'Busy bus' activity on the CD-ROM and the problems-bank examples to develop understanding of this strategy.

Draw a diagram

Rationale

Similar to 'use a tally', drawing a picture or diagram can help children to solve problems as it allows them to visualise a problem more clearly. It also helps them to break down and solve more difficult problems.

Teaching the strategy

Write an appropriate problem on the board, for example:

There are fifteen children playing in the park. Seven are playing football and the rest are playing rounders. How many are playing rounders?

- Say: *One way we can solve this problem is by drawing the children.* Tell the children that drawings need not be complicated and they should only contain enough detail to help solve the problem. Explain that simple shapes or strokes can be used to represent the objects.
- Draw 15 circles on the board and say: *These are fifteen children.*
- Say: *Seven children are playing football so we can write an 'F' for football on seven of the circles.* Write a letter F on seven of the circles.
- Ask the children to count how many 'children' are left.
- Ask: *How can we check to see if we are right? We count one, two... eight and then add the seven who are playing football. The answer is fifteen, so we are correct!*
- Ask the children to represent the problem as a number sentence: 15 - 7 = 8.

Links to

Molly the Monkey
pages 14-15

Gilbert's garden
pages 28-29

Pose other similar problems and ask the children to draw pictures on the board to help solve them. Use the 'Molly the Monkey' and 'Gilbert's garden' activities on the CD-ROM and the problems-bank examples to develop understanding of this strategy.

Trial and improvement

Rationale

This problem-solving strategy allows children to make guesses and then refine their guesses until they reach the correct answer. In this way, they develop logical reasoning. It also develops the understanding that problem solving can be time-consuming and that it is important to persevere. Learning how to work systematically helps children in all of their problem-solving strategies.

Teaching the strategy

Write a sample problem appropriate to the children's age and mathematical ability on the board. For example:

Two numbers when added together come to 15. The two numbers have a difference of 1. What are the two numbers?

- Ask the children to make a guess using the information given in the problem: *Say we guess 10 and 5. They add up to 15, but their difference is too big. The difference is 5 and not 1, so these numbers are not correct.*
- Suggest the children make another guess. *The numbers could be 9 and 6. These numbers add to 15, but there is still too big a difference.* (3)
- Ask the children to keep guessing until they arrive at the correct answer. Highlight the fact that you narrowed the possibilities until the correct answer was found.
- Ask for another guess, leading the children towards the correct answer (8 and 7). Encourage the children to check that the numbers add to 15 and that they have a difference of 1.
- Discuss how incorrect guesses are important steps towards solving a problem or puzzle using this strategy. Highlight the need to work systematically in making guesses.

Use the 'Shape Sudoku', 'Balance beam' and 'Magic coins' activities on the CD-ROM and the problems-bank examples to develop understanding of this strategy.

Links to

Shape Sudoku
pages 20-21

Balance beam
pages 22-23

Magic coins
pages 24-25

Estimation

Rationale

The skill of estimation helps children in all work in mathematics. At this level, children should be encouraged to develop the strategy of 'eyeballing' a small group and using this benchmark to estimate how many are in a larger group. Recognition of patterns in a collection then becomes easier. When checking estimates, children are able to model equal groups. They also develop skills in counting in fives and tens using skip counting. This helps them deal with larger numbers as their skills progress.

It is important to develop an understanding that estimation means that you do not need to count each object. Children need to understand that they are not 'wrong' if they give a 'wrong' answer. Do not therefore emphasise 'right' guesses. The idea behind estimating is to develop the skill of close guessing first, rather than counting first. While children should be encouraged to check if their estimate makes sense in relation to the problem, they need not be required to confirm an estimate by counting. However, you will probably find that they will want to do this anyway.

Teaching the strategy

Try the following ideas for teaching the 'estimation' strategy:

- Model how a benchmark can be used to help children estimate a larger group.
- Put out a group of five objects (for example, books, school bags or marbles). Ask the children to 'see' that it is a group of five objects.
- Put out a larger group of objects (such as 20) and have the children estimate how many are in the group.
- To check the guesses, show how the objects can be put into groups of five and then the groups counted by fives.
- Discuss how much easier this is than counting in ones, especially when big numbers are involved.
- Discuss when, if counting a large number of items, miscounting occurs. It is much easier therefore to count groups of five or ten rather than ones.
- Always encourage children to talk about finding and counting 'in groups of...'.

Links to

Magic coins
pages 24-25

Use the 'Magic coins' activity on the CD-ROM and the problems-bank examples to develop understanding of this strategy.

Look for patterns

Rationale

Looking for patterns is a very important strategy for solving mathematical problems and puzzles. By observing each given element, one at a time in consecutive sequence, children can decide what the next elements will be in the pattern. Predictions based on these patterns can be used to solve many different kinds of problem. The development of these skills during Key Stage 1 will lay the foundation for later algebra work. In these early stages of mathematics learning, children should be given as many opportunities as possible to practise the 'look for patterns' strategy.

Teaching the strategy

Try the following ideas for teaching the 'look for patterns' strategy:

- Write a sample problem on the board, such as: *Luke has written a number pattern that begins 12, 10, 8, 6. If he continues this pattern, what will be the next three numbers?* Ask the children to look for the pattern using the numbers that are given and then to work out the rule. (-2)
- Encourage the children to recognise, copy, continue and create repeating patterns using shapes, objects and pictures. Ask them to describe a repeating pattern made from shapes.
- Encourage the children to describe a repeating pattern in terms of a number (for example, 00*00* is a 'three pattern').
- Ask the children if they can recognise, copy, continue and describe simple number patterns that increase and decrease (for example, 2, 4, 6, 8 or 10, 9, 8, 7). Can they identify and describe patterns when counting forwards or backwards by ones, twos, fives or tens?

Links to

Mind twister
pages 26-27

- Encourage the children to represent number patterns on a 100-square, and to determine missing elements in a number pattern.
- Ask the children to create different patterns and describe the rule.

Use the 'Mind twister' activity on the CD-ROM and the problems-bank examples to develop understanding of this strategy.

Logical reasoning

Rationale

'Logical reasoning' is used when we have to consider many pieces of information, decide what goes where, organise it and address one part at a time. The solving of many types of puzzle from everyday life falls into this category. There are a number of strategies which come under the umbrella of solving problems by 'logical reasoning'. These include trial and improvement, using a diagram, and considering all the information. Chiefly, the children must understand what they are being asked, what information is to be used and in what order it should be utilised.

Teaching the strategy

Write a problem appropriate to the children's mathematical understanding on the board. Consider the following items as you work through it together:

- Ask the children to read the problem and think about it as they read it.
- Underline any keywords. This is the most important step, as the question and the data often contain tricks or twists that can confuse children.
- Plan. Decide what is known and what needs to be found out. Ask: *Have you seen a similar problem? What did you need to do to solve it?*
- Decide on the strategy to be used.
  - Trial and improvement: Before guessing, the children should decide whether the answer will be larger or smaller than the information given, before guessing.
  - Use a diagram to represent objects that must be placed in position.
  - Make a list. This strategy will simplify the data in the problem so that it can be seen more clearly.
- Apply the strategy. The strategies all require some writing down of information. Remind the children to show all their working and write the answer clearly.

Links to

Froggy frenzy
pages 30-31

Use the 'Froggy frenzy' activity on the CD-ROM and the problems-bank examples to develop understanding of this strategy.

Activity no.	Activity title	Page no.	Learning objectives as taken from the Primary Framework for Mathematics		Problem-solving strategies
1	Busy bus	12	Using and applying	Solve problems involving addition and subtraction in context	Act it out Use a tally
			Knowing and using number facts	Derive and recall all addition and subtraction facts for each number to at least 10	
2	Molly the Monkey	14	Using and applying	Solve problems involving subtraction in context of numbers	Draw a diagram
			Knowing and using number facts	Use knowledge of number facts and operations to check answers	
3	A dog's dinner	16	Using and applying	Identify the calculation needed to solve a problem; carry out the steps and check the solution in the context of the problem	Act it out
			Calculating	Use practical and informal written methods and related vocabulary to support division, including calculations with remainders	
4	Honey's money	18	Using and applying	Identify and record a calculation needed to solve a problem; carry out the steps or calculations and check the solution in context	Act it out
			Knowing and using number facts	Use knowledge of number facts and operations to check answers to calculations	
5	Shape Sudoku	20	Using and applying	Follow a line of enquiry; answer questions by selecting and organising information in tables and simple diagrams	Trial and improvement
			Understanding shape	Follow and give instructions involving position	
6	Balance beam	22	Using and applying	Describe patterns involving numbers, make predictions and test these with examples	Trial and improvement
			Knowing and using number facts	Derive and recall addition and subtraction facts for all pairs with totals to 20	
7	Magic coins	24	Using and applying	Describe relationships involving numbers	Trial and improvement Estimation
			Counting and understanding number	Order two-digit numbers and position them on a number line	
8	Mind twister	26	Using and applying	Describe patterns and relationships, make predictions and test these with examples	Look for patterns
			Understanding shape	Follow and give instructions involving position	
9	Gilbert's garden	28	Using and applying	Describe patterns involving shapes; make predictions and test with examples	Draw a diagram
			Understanding shape	Visualise common 2D shapes; identify shapes in different positions and orientations	
10	Froggy frenzy	30	Using and applying	Present solutions to problems in an organised way; explain decisions and methods in pictorial, spoken or written form	Logical reasoning
			Understanding shape	Follow and give instructions involving direction and movement	

Busy bus

Learning objectives

- **Using and applying:** Solve problems involving addition and subtraction in context
- **Knowing and using number facts:** Derive and recall all addition and subtraction facts for each number to at least 10

Problem-solving strategies

Act it out
Use a tally

Setting the scene

This activity is suitable for the whole class. However, after initially 'acting it out' as a class, the problem might also be carried out by groups or paired workers. It involves two-step problems with a number range to 10. Children need to keep track of how many passengers there will be on a bus each time people get on or off. You have the option of dragging passengers on and off the bus, counting on or back at each bus stop, or of using other methods to work out the total and simply entering the answer on-screen, whereupon the bus will automatically move on to the next stop.

Solving the problem

Act out the problem by setting up a 'bus' with ten chairs in the centre of the classroom. Ask the children whether they would add or subtract when people get on or off the bus, before acting out the problem and counting the new number on the bus. Move on to the software and at each bus stop, act out the problem in the class before asking individual children to come to the whiteboard to drag and drop the required number of passengers on and off the bus and type in the correct number.

The problem could also be carried out by asking the children to keep a tally of those on the bus, using the template on page 13. Alternatively, show how to use number sentences, focusing on one step of the problem at a time. Write two separate number sentences - one addition and one subtraction - each time the bus stops.

Key questions

Representing: *What calculation will you do if people get on / off the bus?*
Communicating: *Can you write a number sentence to represent eight people on the bus, three people getting off and one getting on?*

Differentiation

Less confident: Work with the children, using the method of dragging passengers on and off the bus at each stop before entering the answer. Provide them with copies of page 13 to keep a tally if necessary, and support strategies for counting on and back.
More confident: Encourage the children to work out how many passengers will be on the bus at each stop without dragging them on or off. Challenge them to write number sentences for the two-step problems. For example, if there are six people on the bus and the problem is 'five people get off the bus and three get on', say: *Five people get off the bus,* and write 6 - 5 = 1. Then say, *Next three people get on the bus,* and write 1 + 3 = 4. If appropriate, go on to model that therefore 6 - 5 + 3 = 4.

Follow up

Ask the children to use the grids on page 13 to make up similar problems for a partner. They should take turns to suggest the number of people already on the bus and then the number getting on or off.

Problems bank

Pages 34 and 35

1. Drag passengers on and off the bus.

2. Enter answer and click 'OK'. If required, enter answer without dragging passengers and the bus moves on automatically.

Name ______________________ Date ______________

Busy bus

Molly the Monkey

Learning objectives

- **Using and applying:** Solve problems involving subtraction in context of numbers
- **Knowing and using number facts:** Use knowledge of number facts and operations to check answers

Problem-solving strategy

Draw a diagram

Setting the scene

In this whole-class activity the children need to identify the different stages of subtraction problems. To help their understanding, the initial set of problems is presented using a diagram in which the numbers are represented by coconuts.

Once Molly the Monkey reaches the top of the tree, a new and different set of problems is presented. No images of coconuts are given on screen to help for this second set, so the children may wish to represent the problem by drawing (on their individual whiteboards) the coconuts that each monkey has. This activity reinforces the language associated with subtraction.

Solving the problem

Solving the problem is straightforward. The aim of presenting it in various ways is to help children's understanding through a variety of approaches in the early stages of subtraction. You may wish to encourage the children to write down their solutions, using a number sentence each time.

Key questions

Enquiring: *How many coconuts does each monkey have? How many more does Max have than Molly? How many coconuts did they have altogether?*
Communicating: *Can you write down the number sentence for subtracting the coconuts?*

Differentiation

Less confident: Use counting on at each stage initially, to reinforce children's subtraction skills.
More confident: Encourage the children to make up similar problems for each other, using up to 20 coconuts.

2. Enter final answer.

3. Second set of questions don't include images of coconuts.

1. Enter answers to questions at top of screen.

Follow up

Use the subtraction activity on page 15, allowing children to use practical resources to represent the coconuts. If appropriate, move children on to working without the practical resources.

Problems bank

Page 36

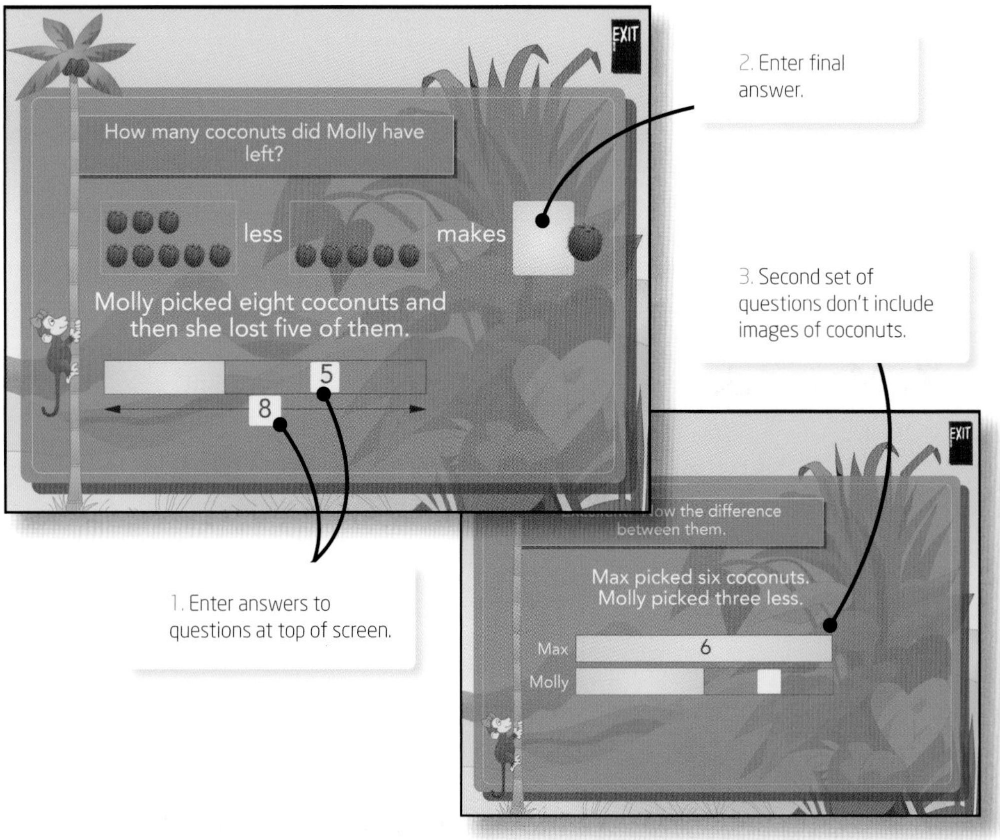

Name ______________________________ Date ____________________

Coconuts

■ How many coconuts did Molly pick each time?

1. Max picked 5 coconuts, and Molly picked 2 fewer.

2. Max picked 12 coconuts, and Molly picked 5 fewer.

3. Max picked 20 coconuts, and Molly picked 8 fewer.

4. Max picked 16 coconuts, and Molly picked 8 fewer.

5. Max picked 22 coconuts, and Molly picked 2 fewer.

6. Max picked 25 coconuts, and Molly picked 4 fewer.

7. Max picked 22 coconuts, and Molly picked 12 fewer.

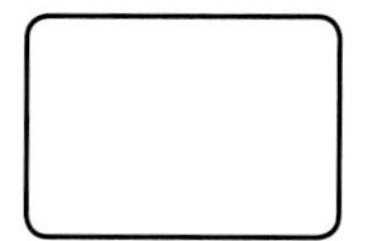

8. Max picked 24 coconuts, and Molly picked 8 fewer.

A dog's dinner

Learning objectives

- **Using and applying:** Identify the calculation needed to solve a problem; carry out the steps and check the solution in the context of the problem
- **Calculating:** Use practical and informal written methods and related vocabulary to support division, including calculations with remainders

Problem-solving strategy

Act it out

Setting the scene

This is a whole-class activity. Fido wants to know how many sausages he will be left with after everyone has had their share. This activity enables children to 'act out' the problem by dragging and dropping the correct number of sausages to the plates and then counting the number left on the tray.

Solving the problem

Use the 'act it out' strategy by dragging the sausages to the plates. Show the children how they can check their results by counting the number of sausages before they are shared out, then recounting the number on each plate and checking that the number of sausages they started with has not changed. Check the children's counting skills while they are carrying out the activity. Encourage them to identify the sharing process as division and, if appropriate, record the solution to the problem using the ÷ and = signs.

Key questions

Enquiring: *How many sausages are there to start with?*
Reasoning: *Have you checked that everyone (including Fido) has the correct number of sausages? How can you check your results?*
Communicating: *Can you tell me a short story about how the sausages were shared out?*

Differentiation

Less confident: Once the solution is found, encourage the children to count the number of sausages on each plate to check that they are correct.
More confident: Challenge the children to work out the answer to the problem without acting it out, and then use the activity to check their solution.

2. Enter answer and click 'OK'.

1. Drag sausages from the tray onto the plates and bowl.

Follow up

Set up a similar practical activity for children to work at in groups of four, using bricks or counters so that each child has a role to play. They should take it in turns to do the sharing out, using the problems on page 17.

Problems bank

Page 37

Name ______________________ Date ______________

A dog's dinner

1.

If each person gets 3 sausages, how many for Fido?........ 

2.

If each person gets 4 sausages, how many for Fido?........ 

3.

If each person gets 3 sausages, how many for Fido?........ 

4.

If each person gets 2 sausages, how many for Fido?........ 

5.

If each person gets 5 sausages, how many for Fido?........

Honey's money

Learning objectives

- **Using and applying:** Identify and record a calculation needed to solve a problem; carry out the steps or calculations and check the solution in context
- **Knowing and using number facts:** Use knowledge of number facts and operations to check answers to calculations

Problem-solving strategy

Act it out

Setting the scene

This whole-class activity provides a lot of opportunity for early number work using addition and subtraction in context. Challenge the children to help Honey to keep track of her money by working out whether she gives or receives money in a series of situations. They must first decide on the correct sign (+ or -) before dragging Honey's money onto or off the table. Be aware that if one answer is incorrect then Honey falls through the trapdoor and she has to start all over again.

Solving the problem

Start by asking the children how much money Honey has on the table initially and count this with them; then discuss the problem and whether to add or subtract. After dragging and dropping the money, count again to see how much Honey finally has on the table. Provide the children with plastic money to support them in acting out these problems.

Key questions

Representing: *Do you think Honey will have less or more money? Do you think you should add to or take away from Honey's money?*
Communicating: *Can you tell me how much money Honey had to start with? Why did she finish with less* (or *more*) *money at the end of the problem?*

Differentiation

Less confident: Support the children in understanding each question. Ask them to look for the key words which will tell them whether they have to add or subtract money.
More confident: Encourage the children to work out the problem mentally before dragging and dropping the coins to check their answer.

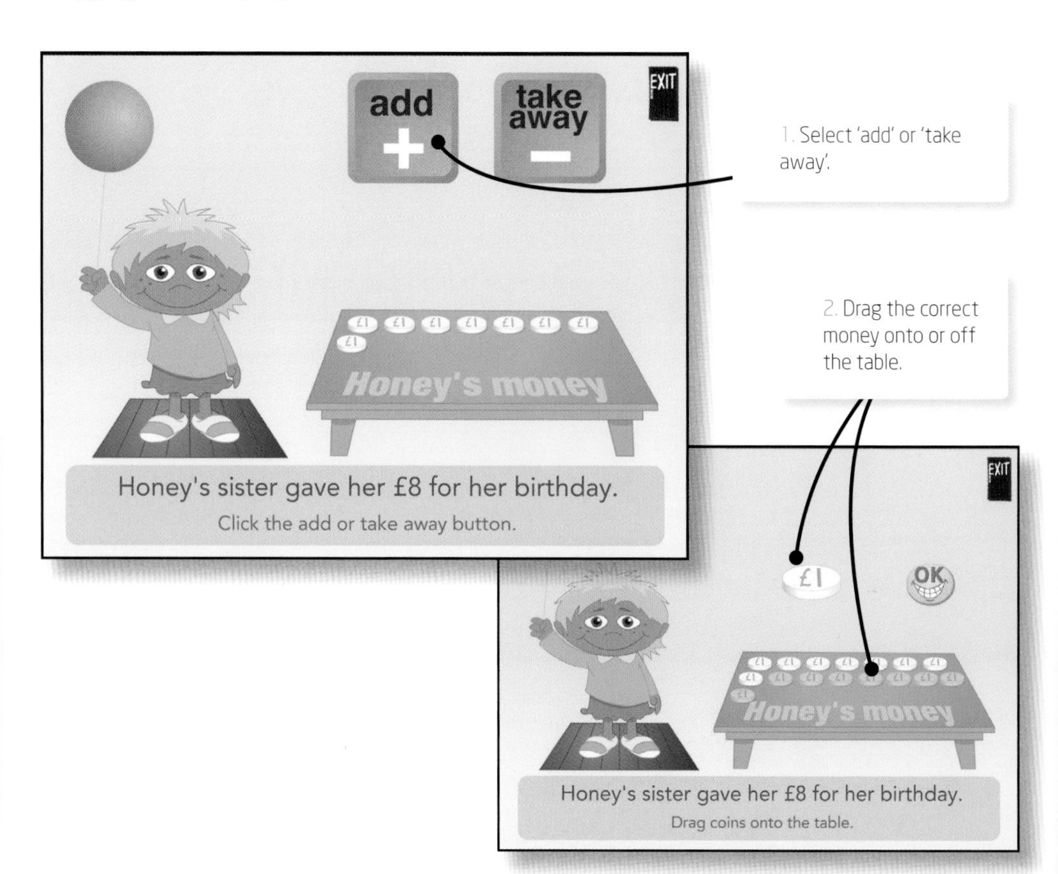

Follow up

Give groups of children some plastic money and use the questions on page 19 to practise the activity through practical work.

Problems bank

Page 38

Name ______________________ Date ______________

Honey's money

- Read each question carefully. Tick the box to show whether to add or subtract, then fill in the gaps in the number sentence.

1. Honey has £19 and she gets £8 for her birthday. How much has she now?

Add	Subtract

Fill in the gaps: 19 ______ 8 = ______

2. Honey has £18 and her Granny gives her £5. How much has she now?

Add	Subtract

Fill in the gaps: 18 ______ 5 = ______

3. Honey has £15 and she spends £9 on her Dad's birthday present. How much has she now?

Add	Subtract

Fill in the gaps: 15 ______ 9 = ______

4. Honey has £17 in her piggy bank and puts £12 in her purse. How much has she got left in her piggy bank?

Add	Subtract

Fill in the gaps: 17 ______ 12 = ______

Shape Sudoku

Learning objectives

- **Using and applying:** Follow a line of enquiry; answer questions by selecting and organising information in tables and simple diagrams
- **Understanding shape:** Follow and give instructions involving position

Problem-solving strategy

Trial and improvement

Setting the scene

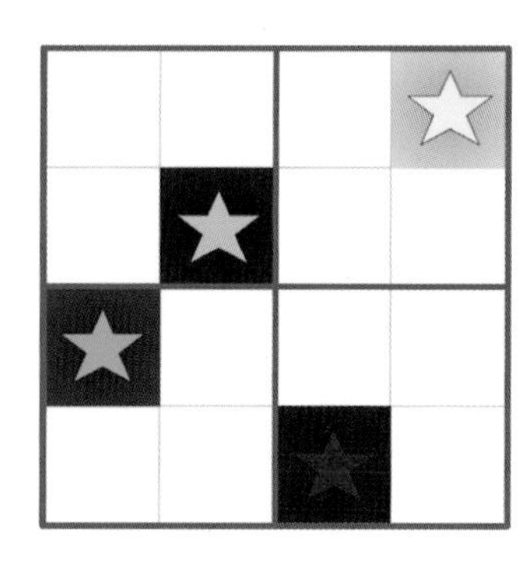

This activity is suitable for groups or paired workers, but it also works well as a whole-class exercise.

This is a simplified version of the usual number-based Sudoku. For a correct solution, each row, column and 2 × 2 square must contain only one star of each colour. If players submit a result and it is incorrect, the problem starts all over again; however, as with any Sudoku puzzle, this is often easier than trying to adapt a wrong solution. Some children show unexpected ability in solving this kind of problem.

Solving the problem

This activity provides an excellent opportunity for using the language to describe position, particularly if using the activity with the whiteboard, because the children will need to tell you where they want to place a colour. You may wish to label each square to make identification easier, for example: rows A, B, C, D and columns 1, 2, 3, 4. There are, of course, many solutions but for a systematic approach there is one easier way to solve the problem. Start by putting the first colour, such as yellow, in different rows and columns, making sure that it only appears once in each small square. Continue this strategy with the next colour, then the third and the fourth. This systematic approach takes away some of the intrigue of guessing and checking, but at the same time it removes some of the frustration of continually getting it wrong.

Key questions

Enquiring: *Have you checked that the position you have chosen for the yellow star is suitable? Why can't the yellow star be placed where suggested? Have you checked that the complete solution you are going to finish with is correct?*
Communicating: *Can you describe the square where you want to place the red star? What is wrong with this suggestion? / Why do you claim it is correct?*

Differentiation

Less confident: Use the follow-up worksheet on page 21 before carrying out the on-screen activity as this is an easier problem. Keep encouraging the children to check their solutions as they work through the on-screen problem to avoid them getting too frustrated by only finding their errors at the end.
More confident: Challenge the children to think of any other systematic approaches they can use to help them to solve the problem.

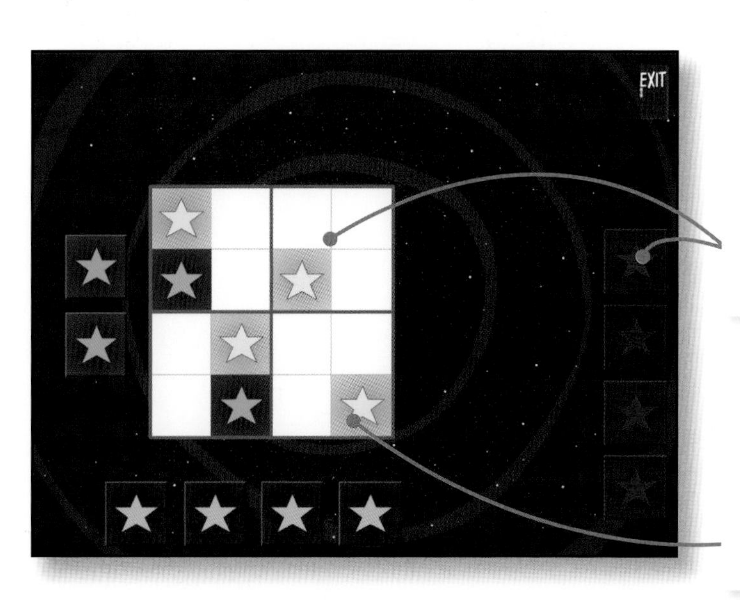

1. Drag the coloured stars and drop them into appropriate places in the grid.

2. Drag the stars to rearrange them within the grid as required.

Follow up

Ask the children to solve the follow-up problem on page 21.

Problems bank

Page 39

Name ______________________ Date ______________

Teddy Sudoku

- 9 teddies live in Teddy Town.
  3 are red, 3 are blue and 3 are yellow.
  There is only one of each colour in each row and column.
- Colour the teddy bears.

Balance beam

Learning objectives

- **Using and applying:** Describe patterns involving numbers, make predictions and test these with examples
- **Knowing and using number facts:** Derive and recall addition and subtraction facts for all pairs with totals to 20

Problem-solving strategy

Trial and improvement

Setting the scene

This activity is suitable for groups, paired workers or the whole class. It challenges children's knowledge of number bonds to 20. The aim is to balance both sides of the three scales shown on screen by dragging and dropping the numbers given at the bottom.

Solving the problem

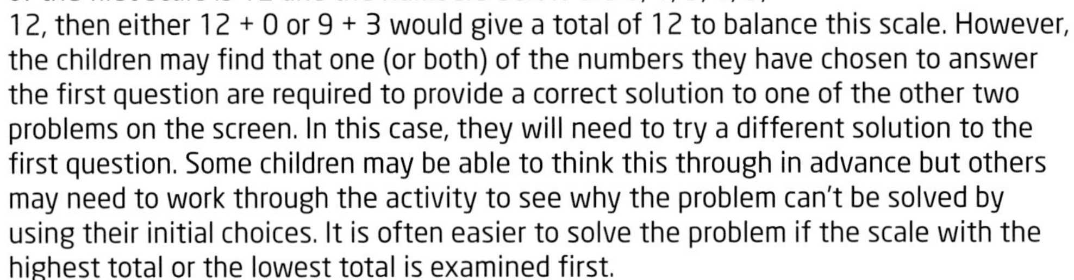

The trial-and-improvement strategy arises since there may be more than one way of balancing the first scale with the numbers given. For example, if the total on the left-hand side of the first scale is 12 and the numbers below are 0, 1, 3, 6, 9, 12, then either 12 + 0 or 9 + 3 would give a total of 12 to balance this scale. However, the children may find that one (or both) of the numbers they have chosen to answer the first question are required to provide a correct solution to one of the other two problems on the screen. In this case, they will need to try a different solution to the first question. Some children may be able to think this through in advance but others may need to work through the activity to see why the problem can't be solved by using their initial choices. It is often easier to solve the problem if the scale with the highest total or the lowest total is examined first.

Key questions

Representing: *What must be added to 0, 6, 8, 11, 13 or 15 to make a total of 20?*
Reasoning: *If we use 12 + 0 to balance the first scale, how can we use the other numbers to balance the other two scales?*
Communicating: *If the sum on the second scale is 1, can you describe why it would not be possible to solve the problem using the numbers 12 + 0 for the answer to the first scale?*

Differentiation

Less confident: For children who are having difficulty with adding or subtracting numbers up to 20, use the activity as practice in the simpler task of balancing just one scale.
More confident: Use the activity to challenge children's communication skills by asking them to explain their solution. Then ask them to make up a similar problem using two scales for a partner.

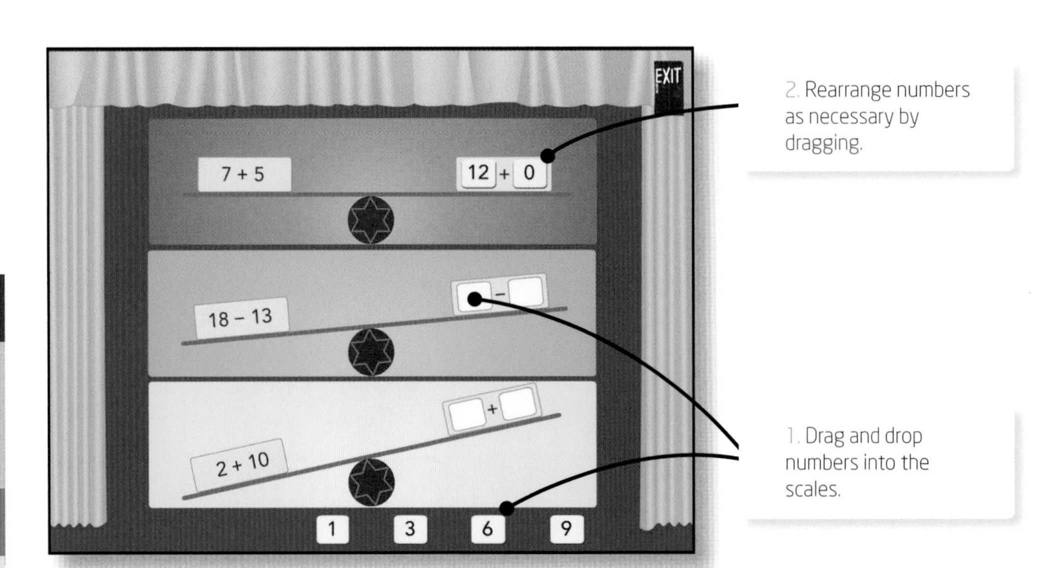

Follow up

Ask the children to use page 23 to set similar problems for a partner.

Problems bank

Page 40

Name ____________________ Date ______________

Balancing act

□ + □ □ + □

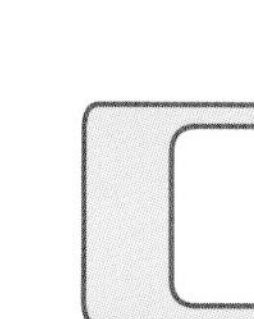

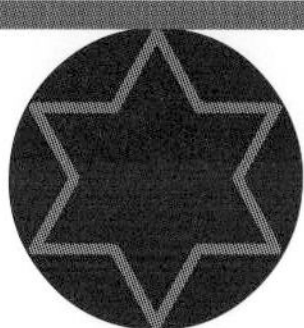

□ + □ □ + □

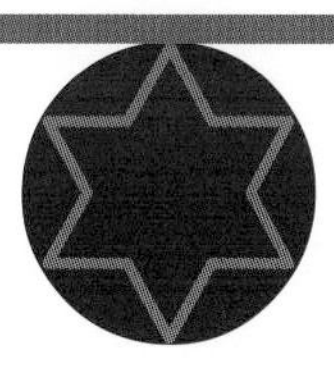

□ + □ □ + □

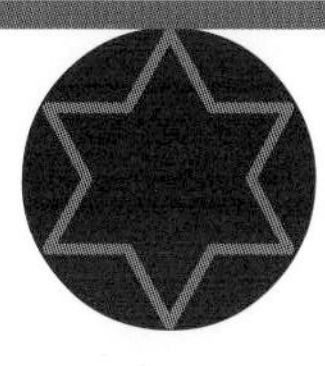

Magic coins

Learning objectives

- **Using and applying:** Describe relationships involving numbers
- **Counting and understanding number:** Order two-digit numbers and position them on a number line

Problem-solving strategies

Trial and improvement
Estimation

Setting the scene

This activity is suitable for the whole class, groups or paired workers. It will help children with vocabulary relating to numbers such as higher/lower or larger/smaller.

The aim is to find out how much money Astrid has in her bag by guessing a number between 1 and 100. Each time a guess is made, players are told whether the number to be found is higher or lower. The children's ability to use the information given provides a good indication of their number capability at this stage. When the correct amount is finally found, the children have to work out what coins Astrid has in her bag. If they are correct, the bucket of water will be tipped over the dragon!

Solving the problem

For Year 2 children, the strategy they use is likely to be based on using the information they already have about the number, and trial and improvement. A good strategy for solving this type of problem, however, is to guess a number 'halfway between' the highest and lowest options known so that the range of the unknown number is always minimised.

Key questions

Representing: *Can you show where the number might be, using a number line?*
Reasoning: *If 18 is too high, why can the number we are guessing not be 21? If 14 is too low, why can the number we are guessing not be 11? If 14 is too low and 18 is too high, what number could the next guess be?*
Communicating: *Can you show how much money Astrid had? What different ways can you show to make the same amount?*

Differentiation

Less confident: Start with numbers between 1 and 20 and use a number line to show the children the order of the numbers so they are not just making wild guesses. Explain that if 14 is too low and 18 is too high, then the number to be guessed must lie between these two.
More confident: Encourage more confident learners to use the 'halfway between' strategy in order to reach the answers more quickly.

Follow up

Encourage the children to play the 'Magic coins' game with a partner, using numbers between 1 and 20. It may help if the child with the hidden number writes this down so they do not forget it, and the child guessing makes a note of the highest and lowest each time so they are not guessing randomly. Use page 25 to reinforce vocabulary relating to numbers.

Problems bank

Page 41

2. Find out whether correct number is higher or lower.

Name ______________________________ Date ____________________

Which number?

■ Write down the correct number each time.

1. Which is the larger number, 12 or 20? .... ☐

2. Which is the larger number, 17 or 6? .... ☐

3. Which is the larger number, 4 or 11? .... ☐

4. Which is the larger number, 15 or 13? .... ☐

5. Which is the larger number, 4 or 19? .... ☐

6. Which is the smaller number, 12 or 72? .... ☐

7. Which is the smaller number, 56 or 48? .... ☐

8. Which is the smaller number, 75 or 57? .... ☐

9. Which is the smaller number, 100 or 10? .... ☐

10. Which is the smaller number, 98 or 89? ...... ☐

Mind twister

Learning objectives

- **Using and applying:** Describe patterns and relationships, make predictions and test these with examples
- **Understanding shape:** Follow and give instructions involving position

Problem-solving strategy

Look for patterns

Setting the scene

This activity is suitable for groups or paired workers. However, as a whole-class activity, it provides a particularly good opportunity to reinforce the language of position.

The aim is to find the matching pairs by clicking on each tile to reveal the hidden image. Once a pair has been found, the tiles are removed. If a pair is not found, the player loses a life. This activity includes two levels, with the second level allowing fewer incorrect answers.

Solving the problem

This is a memory game, so the last tile selected is the most easily remembered. When trying to match a pair, click first on a tile that has not previously been turned over or has not been remembered and then, if it corresponds with a tile that has been remembered, click on that. It is usually easier to remember tiles that are on the corners or the outside of the square than those in the middle. Encourage the children to devise their own strategies for remembering the position of a particular tile (for example, *top left* or *bottom left*).

Key questions

Enquiring: *How do you remember where a particular tile is?*
Reasoning: *What is the matching pair you are trying to find?*
Communicating: *Can you explain to me where you think the matching tile is?*

Differentiation

Less confident: Support children by reinforcing what they have discovered verbally and visually, for example by saying: *So we know that the apple is in the top left-hand corner,* while pointing to the apple. It may help to number each square if the children have real difficulty in describing position.
More confident: Challenge children by moving on to level 2, in which the number of lives available is reduced.

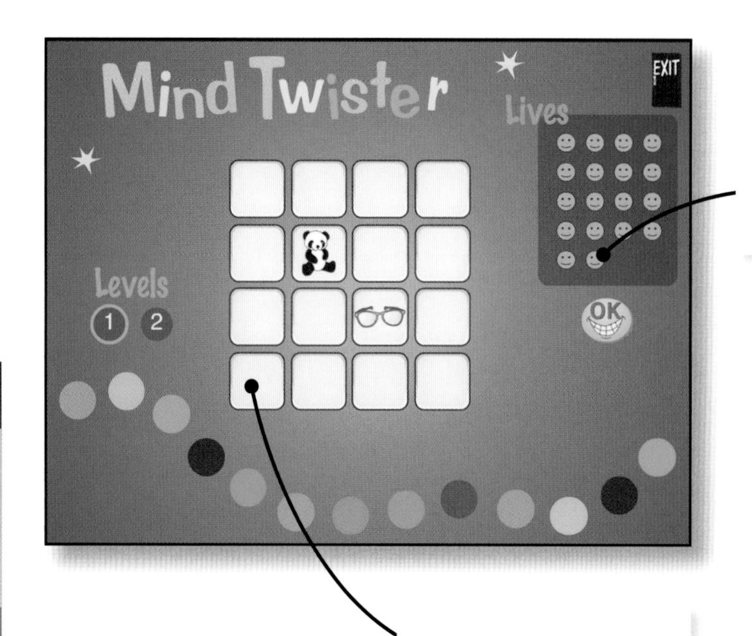

2. A life is lost when a pair is not found.

1. Click on the tiles to reveal the hidden images.

Follow up

Use the matching activity on page 27 to practise the classification of 2D shapes.

Problems bank

Page 42

Name ____________________ Date ____________________

Match the word to the shape

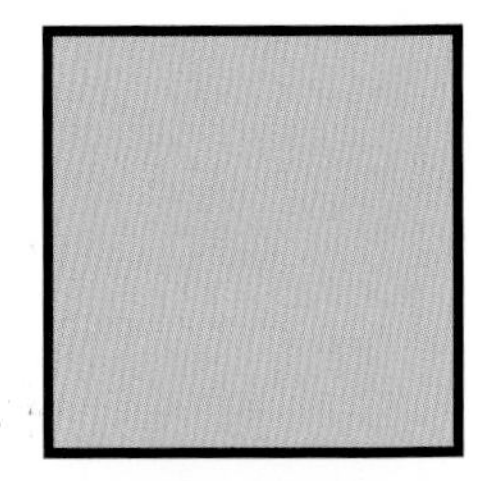

triangle

rectangle

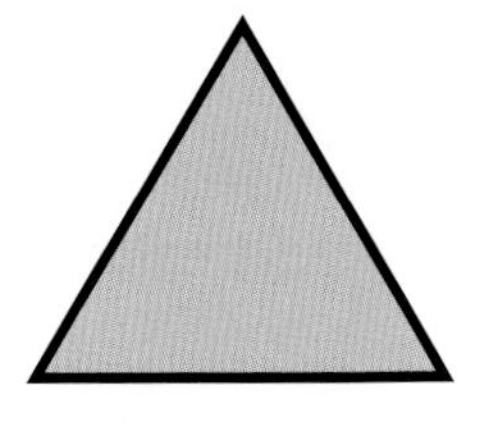

diamond

circle

star

square

Gilbert's garden

Learning objectives

- **Using and applying:** Describe patterns involving shapes; make predictions and test with examples
- **Understanding shape:** Visualise common 2D shapes; identify shapes in different positions and orientations

Problem-solving strategy

Draw a diagram

Setting the scene

This activity is suitable for groups, paired workers or the whole class. Explain that Gilbert is building a wall in his garden and he would like the children to help. In a wheelbarrow he has right-angled triangles, squares and rectangles in assorted colours. The aim of the activity is to drag the different shapes onto Gilbert's wall following the instructions given. For example: *Fill the wall with yellow rectangles and blue squares.*

Solving the problem

When dragged, the shapes click into place once they are close to a suitable position. The whole wall must be completed before moving on. Question the children about the shape they are using (its colour, name and number of sides) to reinforce their understanding of shape. Challenge them to use the same tiles to make a different pattern. If two colours are used, ask them to think about the most interesting pattern they can make before dragging and dropping the shapes into position.

Key questions

Enquiring: *Can you find the shapes from Gilbert's wheelbarrow to make the wall?*
Reasoning: *Can you describe the pattern you have made for Gilbert's wall?*
Communicating: *Can you describe the shapes you have used to make Gilbert's wall?*

Differentiation

Less confident: Support children in distinguishing each shape and colour. Point to each shape in the wheelbarrow and ask: *What is this shape called?* Then discuss the colour of each shape.
More confident: Some questions require a pattern to be made using two colours, which will challenge children's creative abilities.

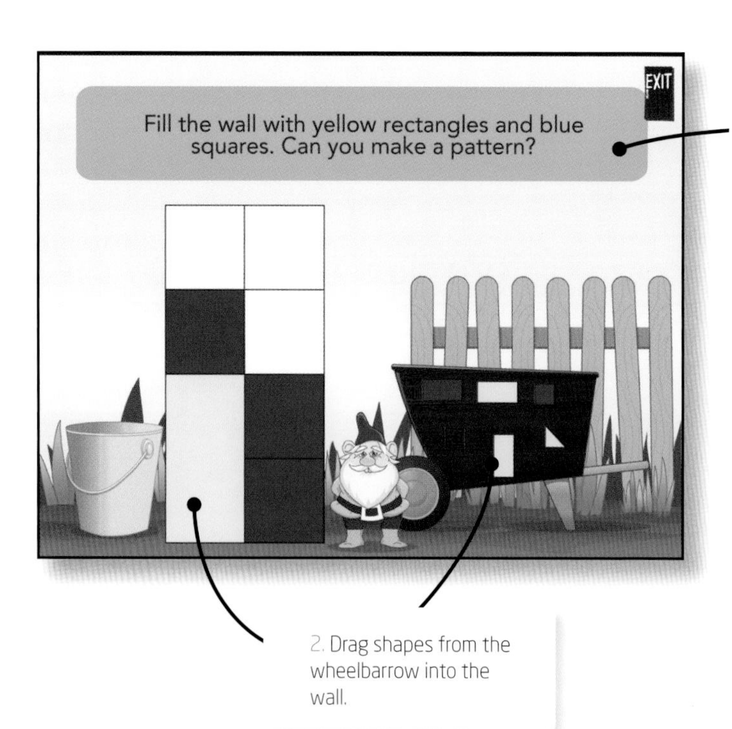

Follow up

Ask the children to colour in their own garden paths using the templates on page 29.

Problems bank

Page 43

Name ______________________ Date ______________

Gilbert's garden paths

- Colour in a pattern for the path in Gilbert's garden.

1. Colour the first rectangle red, the second yellow, the third green, then repeat the pattern.

2. Use two colours (blue and yellow) to make a pattern for the path. Then draw more tiles to continue the pattern.

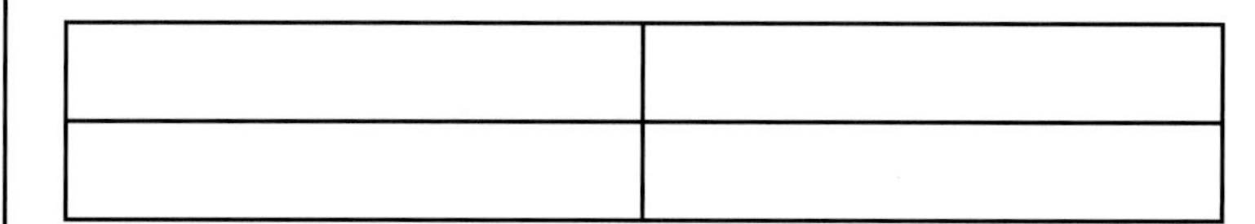

3. Use blue and yellow again to see if you can make a different pattern. Then draw more tiles to continue the pattern.

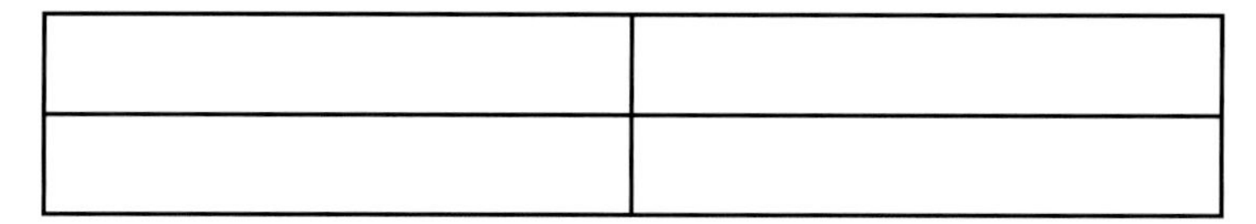

4. Use green and blue to make a pattern by colouring in each square. Then draw more tiles to continue the pattern.

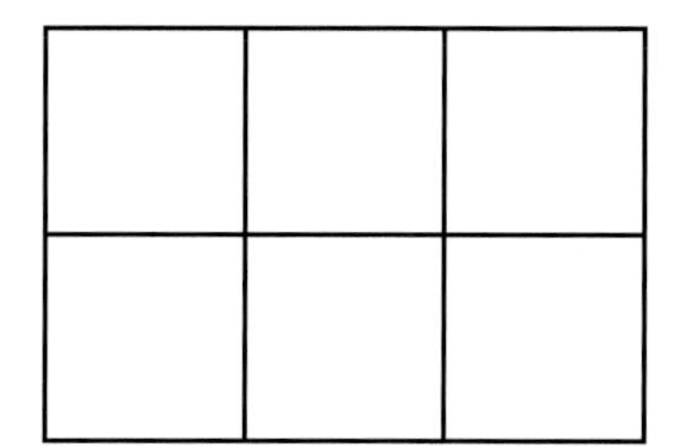

5. Using 2 colours, make up a pattern of your own by colouring in the triangles. Then draw more tiles to continue the pattern.

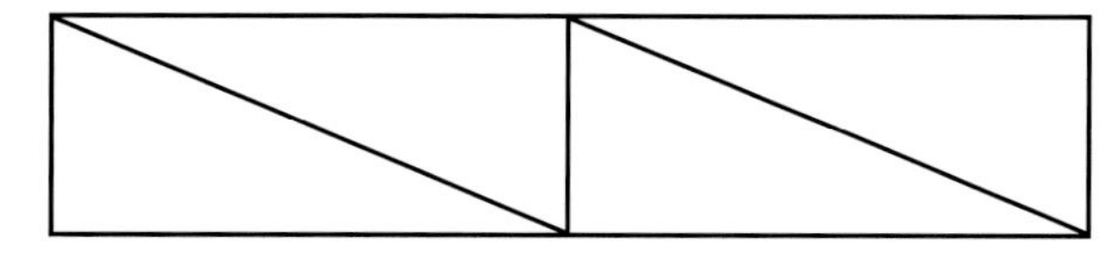

Froggy frenzy

Learning objectives

- **Using and applying:** Present solutions to problems in an organised way; explain decisions and methods in pictorial, spoken or written form
- **Understanding shape:** Follow and give instructions involving direction and movement

Problem-solving strategy

Logical reasoning

Setting the scene

This activity is suitable for groups or paired workers. The aim is to help Froggy to jump from one lily pad to the next by clicking on the arrows and numbers. For each successful jump, a lily pad is collected at the top of the screen. When they have all been collected, the children have to help Froggy back to his island home. Be careful, as one incorrect move and Froggy will end up in the water! Moves must also be made within a time limit or a similar watery fate awaits Froggy.

Solving the problem

Encourage the children to think through the directions they want to take to reach each lily pad. Movement, especially to the left or right, might be intuitive to some children but others may find it more difficult. Also, on some occasions, children need to plot a course between three lily pads, which requires a higher level of logical reasoning. Remind them that '0' will sometimes be the correct number to select.

Key questions

Enquiring: *Which would be the shortest route to move from one lily pad to another?*
Reasoning: *Can you estimate how many steps it would take to move from this lily pad to the other lily pad? Are there any alternative routes to move between the two lily pads? Does it make any difference if you move up and down or left and right first? Why/why not? How could you check the number of steps you took between different lily pads?* (Suggest the use of the follow-up grids on page 31 for checking purposes.)

Differentiation

Less confident: Work with the children to complete the activity at the whiteboard, focusing on just one or two examples initially. Support them with the correct mathematical vocabulary if necessary.
More confident: Set a time limit for the children to complete all seven moves.

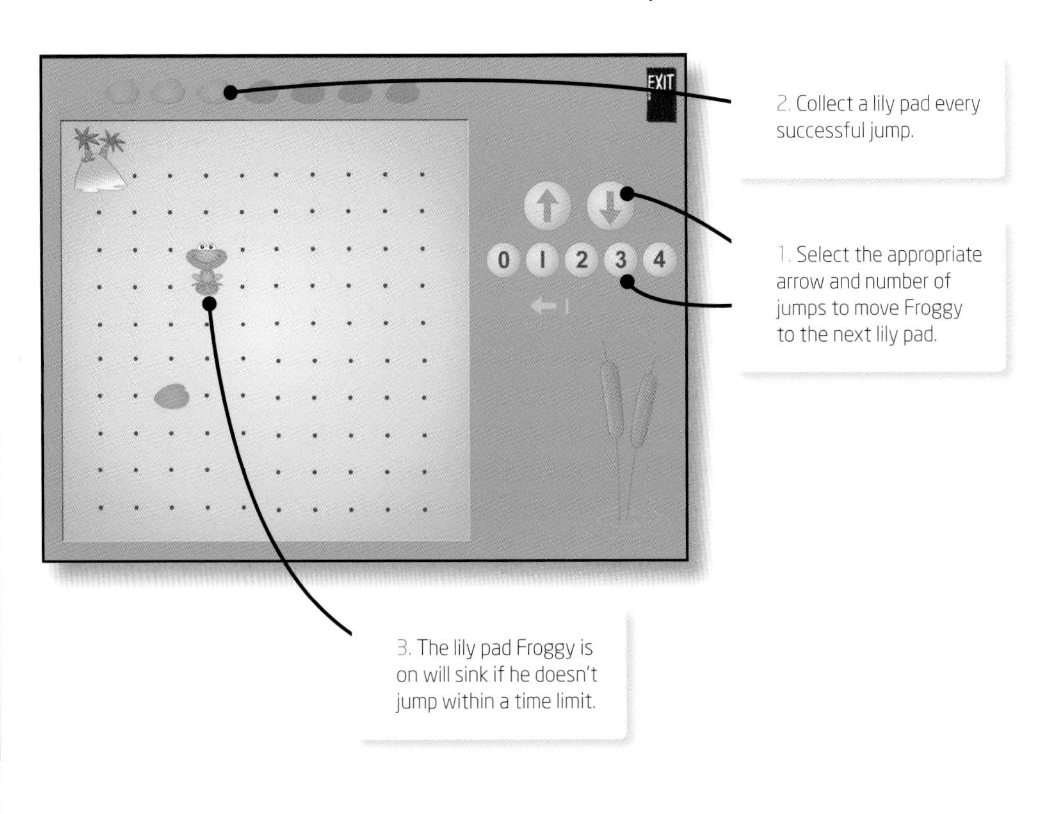

2. Collect a lily pad every successful jump.

1. Select the appropriate arrow and number of jumps to move Froggy to the next lily pad.

3. The lily pad Froggy is on will sink if he doesn't jump within a time limit.

Follow up

Let the children use the grids provided on page 31 to plot the route between different lily pads. Ask them to write down the routes they have selected. Challenge one child to prepare a route for a second child to follow. The CD also includes versions with 5 × 5 grids and 20 × 20 grids for additional support or extension activities.

Problems bank

Page 44

Name ______________________ Date ______________

Froggy grids

- Make a route for Froggy to follow.

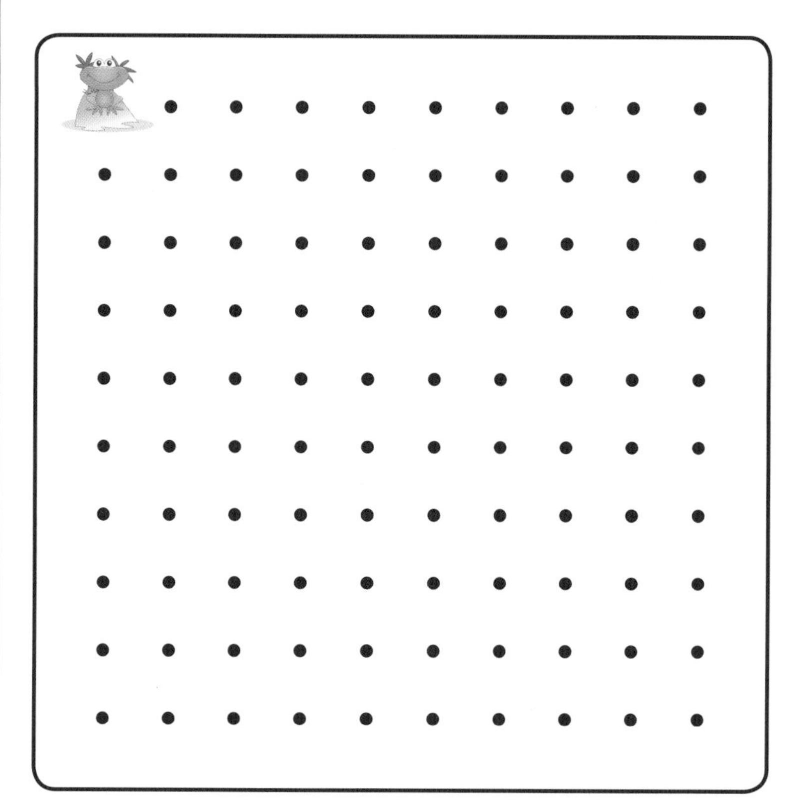

Routes ______________________

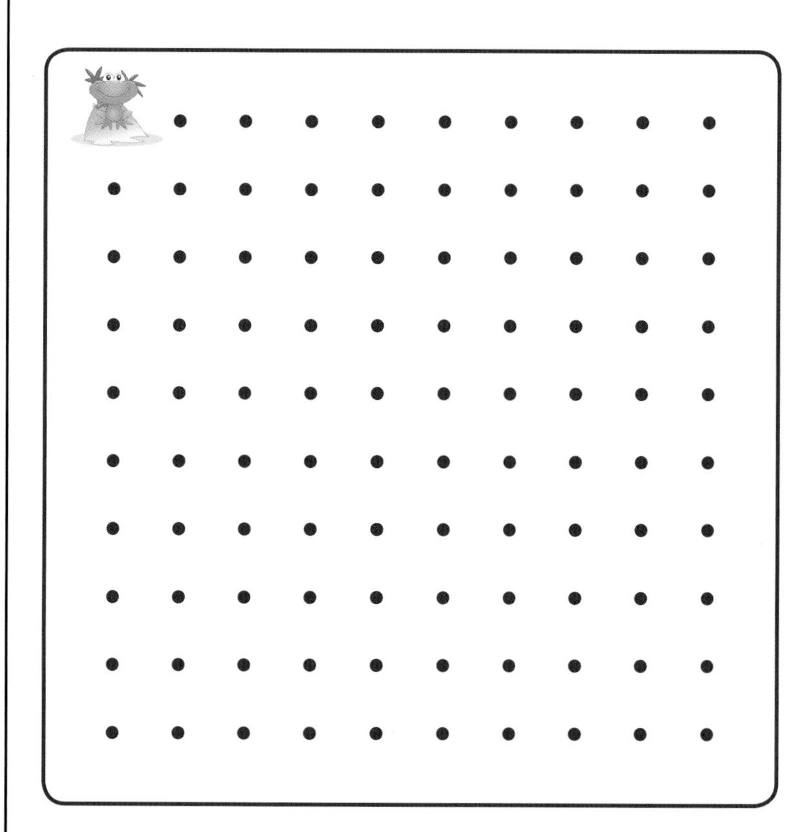

Routes ______________________

Problems bank overview

How many? — Page 34

Problem-solving strategies: Act it out/Use a tally

This activity contains three problems: **1** calculating the number of coins in a set amount; **2** addition and subtraction; **3** finding a total amount in pence.

Vocabulary: *how many?, costs, altogether, are left, pence*

Linked to activity: Busy bus

Bookworm — Page 35

Problem-solving strategy: Use a tally

This problem involves addition and subtraction.

Vocabulary: *addition, how many more?, subtraction*

Linked to activity: Busy bus

The stairs — Page 36

Problem-solving strategy: Draw a diagram

Vocabulary: *bottom, second, middle, higher*

Linked to activity: Molly the Monkey

Mr Snail — CD only

Problem-solving strategy: Draw a diagram

Vocabulary: *metres, up, down, how long?, add, subtract, count*

Linked to activity: Molly the Monkey

Who sits where? — Page 37

Problem-solving strategy: Act it out

The children can work in groups of nine or ten. Nine children take the name of a child from the problem and they use the clues to find out where each child sits. Remind the children to record the solution before they move.

Vocabulary: *between, in front of, behind*

Linked to activity: A dog's dinner

Time problems — CD only

Problem-solving strategy: Act it out

Two problems: **1** counting on or subtraction (answer in hours); **2** counting on.

Vocabulary: *counting on, how long?, add, subtract, hours, how many?*

Linked to activity: A dog's dinner

Buttons / Balloons — Page 38

Problem-solving strategy: Act it out

This activity contains two problems.

Vocabulary: *how many?, add, lots of*

Linked to activity: Honey's money

25 pence — Page 39

Problem-solving strategy: Trial and improvement

There are a number of different solutions to this problem. Encourage multiple answers.

Vocabulary: *too much, not enough, coins, what coins?*

Linked to activity: Shape Sudoku

Problems bank overview

Book balance — Page 40

Problem-solving strategy: Trial and improvement

Tell the children they can use two or more piles together, as long as each pile is used just once in each combination.

Vocabulary: *balance, pile, add, total*

Linked to activity: Balance beam

What number am I? / Pocket money — Page 41

Problem-solving strategies: Trial and improvement / Estimation

Vocabulary: *even, less, one-digit, what number?, twice, between, how much?*

Linked to activity: Magic coins

Hungry snails — Page 42

Problem-solving strategy: Look for patterns

Children recognise and continue a simple number pattern, and give the rule.

Vocabulary: *number pattern, what is the rule?*

Linked to activity: Mind twister

Baked beans — CD only

Problem-solving strategy: Look for patterns

Children identify and continue a pattern, and give the rule.

Vocabulary: *number pattern, what is the rule?*

Linked to activity: Mind twister

Grid patterns — Page 43

Problem-solving strategy: Draw a diagram

Children must draw their own patterns. They should be simple so that they can be repeated easily.

Vocabulary: *ordinal numbers, position words, names of shapes (square, circle, triangle), names for lines (wavy, oblique, diagonal, repeat)*

Linked to activity: Gilbert's garden

Crummy calculator — Page 44

Problem-solving strategy: Logical reasoning

A thinking exercise of everyday problem solving. How can I do something when the mechanism does not work? There is always a way. These problems reinforce some number concepts such as $9 \times 6 = 9 \times 5 + 9 \times 1$. This would be one way to cope with the malfunction of the '6'.

Linked to activity: Froggy frenzy

Minibeast races — CD only

Problem-solving strategy: Logical reasoning

Reading the problem carefully is paramount. Read the problems aloud and question the children's comprehension. Pausing at correct places to obtain best meaning is important to young children. Ask them to work through the data, placing names in the appropriate shapes in each line. When they have finished, encourage them to check that they are correct by re-reading the problem and confirming that the picture correctly illustrates what has been read.

Linked to activity: Froggy frenzy

Name ______________________ Date ______________

How many?

1. Cathy has £1.

A flower costs 20p.

How many flowers can she buy?

Answer ______________________

2. Michael borrowed 15 books from the library.

He reads one every night.

How many books are left to read after one week?

Answer ______________________

3. Ben has four £1 coins, five 10p coins and two 5p coins.

How many pence does he have altogether?

Answer ______________________

Name ______________________ Date ______________

Bookworm

- On Monday, Bookworm borrowed 20 books from the library.
- He read one book when he got home.
  On Tuesday, he read two books.
  On Wednesday he read three books.
  On Thursday he read two books, and on Friday he read four more books.
  On Saturday he read another four books.
  On Sunday he counted the books he had read.

1. How many books had he read?

Answer ______________________

2. How many books did he have to read before he took them all back to the library?

Answer ______________________

Name ______________________ Date ______________

The stairs

Jim is at the bottom of the stairs.

Tom is on the second stair.

Suri is at the top. She is five stairs higher than Tom.

Andy is on the middle stair.

How many stairs are there? ______________________

What stair is Andy on? ______________________

Name ____________________ Date ____________________

Who sits where?

Ben

- Ben sits between Lily and Sunil and in front of Dan.
- Kai sits behind Sunil.
- Ruby sits in front of Lily.
- Jamie sits between Ruby and Kate.

1. Write the children's names on their desks.

2. Where does Simon sit? ____________________

Name ______________________ Date ______________

Buttons

Mother Bear made new coats for her 5 bear cubs. The coats have 3 buttons each.

How many buttons does Mother Bear need?

Answer ______________________

Balloons

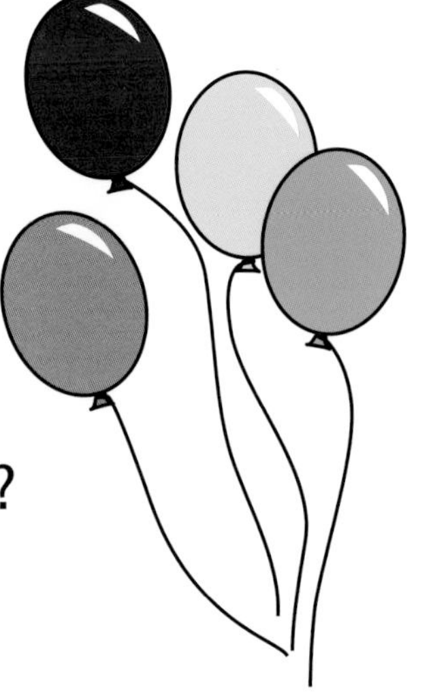

Paula had 8 blue balloons.

She blew up some more balloons – 4 red, 5 yellow, 4 purple, 9 orange, 6 green and 2 white.

How many balloons did Paula have altogether?

Answer ______________________

Name ______________________ Date ______________

25 pence

Sim was given 25p by her gran.

What coins could Sim's gran have given her?

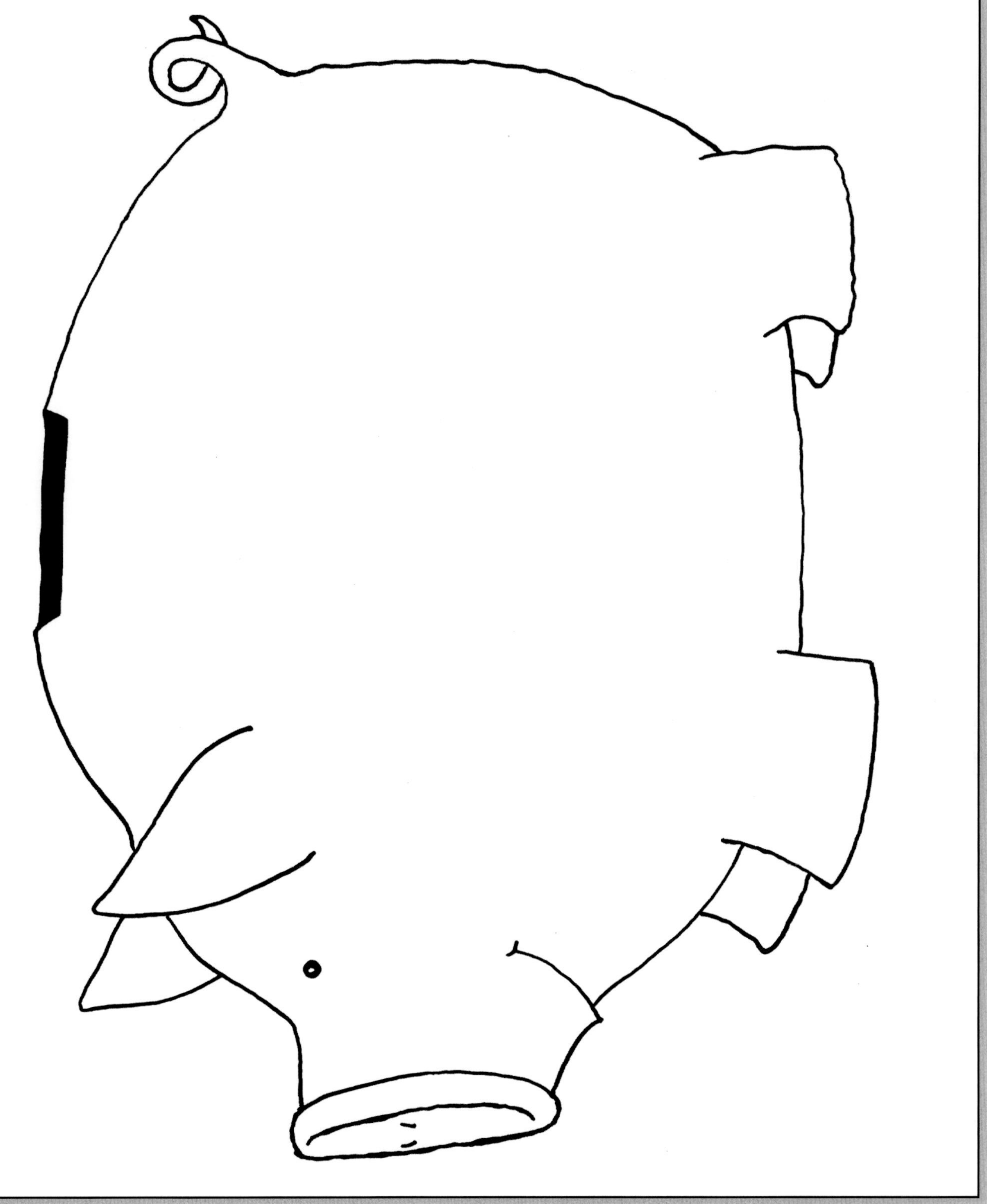

Name ______________________ Date ______________

Book balance

Which piles of books could be used to balance the ten books?

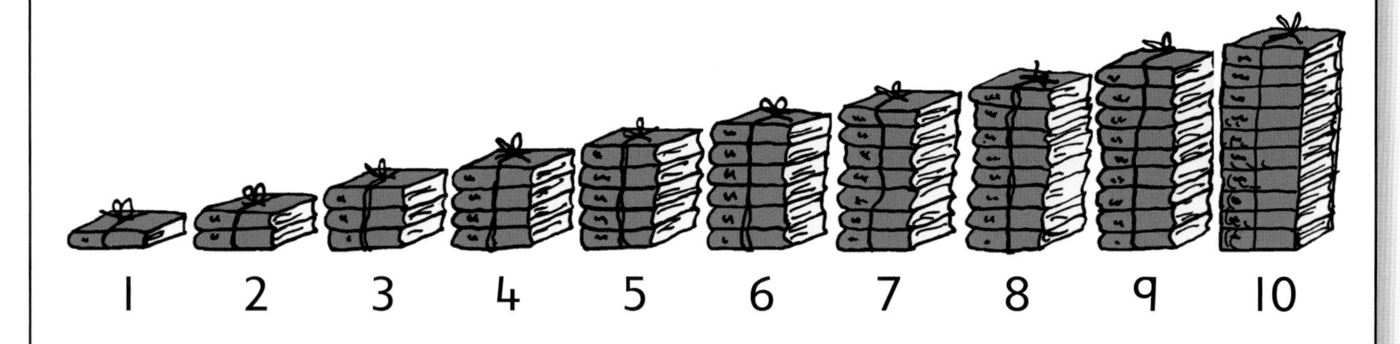

Name ______________________ Date ______________

What number am I?

I am even.

I am less than 20.

I have 2 digits.

One digit is twice the other.

What number am I?

Answer ______________________

Pocket money

Reece and Luke are given £13 pocket money between them each month.

Reece gets £5 more than Luke.

How much pocket money does each get?

Reece ______________________

Luke ______________________

Name ______________________ Date ______________

Hungry snails

Ben planted 30 lettuces.

Each night snails ate some of his lettuces.

On Monday there were **28** lettuces left.

On Tuesday there were **26** lettuces left.

On Wednesday there were ______ lettuces left.

On Thursday there were **22** lettuces left.

On Friday there were ______ lettuces left.

On Saturday there were ______ lettuces left.

On Sunday there were ______ lettuces left.

On ________________ there were ______ lettuces left.

On ________________ there were ______ lettuces left.

On ________________ there were ______ lettuces left.

On ________________ there were ______ lettuces left.

What is the rule? ______________________________

Name ________________ Date ________________

Grid patterns

- Here's a tile pattern for the floor in Toby Tornado's playroom.

- Complete this tile pattern:

- Use shapes or lines on the blank tiles to make your own patterns. Describe them.

Name ______________________________ Date ____________________

Crummy calculator

- Every day, a different key on my calculator breaks but the number can still appear in the display. How can I get correct answers if I cannot use the broken key?

1. The [7] is broken. Write down my different method.

(a) 3 + 7 + 11 = ______________________________

(b) 6 + 4 + 17 = ______________________________

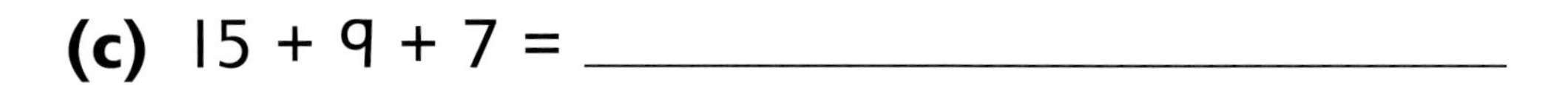

(c) 15 + 9 + 7 = ______________________________

(d) 7 + 7 = ______________________________

2. The [9] is broken. Write down my different method.

(a) 53 – 19 = ______________________________

(b) 67 – 9 – 4 = ______________________________

(c) 164 – 39 = ______________________________

(d) 99 – 2 = ______________________________

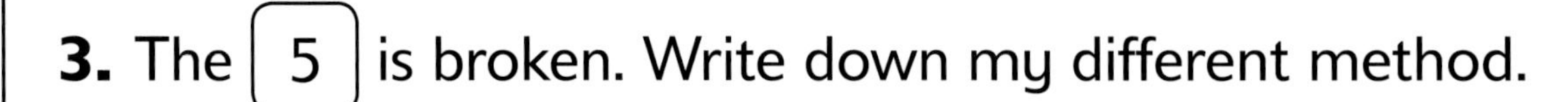

3. The [5] is broken. Write down my different method.

(a) 55 + 5 = ______________________________

(b) 35 – 15 = ______________________________

(c) 52 + 15 + 5 = ______________________________

(d) 50 – 45 + 25 = ______________________________

Teacher's name ____________________

Star Maths Puzzles and Problems diary page

Activity title	Children who used activity	How was activity used	Date used

Activities answers

Busy bus - page 13
Teacher check

Coconuts - page 15
1. 3
2. 7
3. 12
4. 8
5. 20
6. 21
7. 10
8. 16

A dog's dinner - page 17
1. 1
2. 0
3. 6
4. 4
5. 2

Honey's money - page 19
1. (Add) + 27
2. (Add) + 23
3. (Subtract) - 6
4. (Subtract) - 5

Teddy Sudoku - page 21
Teacher check

Balancing act - page 23
Teacher check

Which number? - page 25
1. 20
2. 17
3. 11
4. 15
5. 19
6. 12
7. 48
8. 57
9. 10
10. 89

Match the word to the shape - page 27

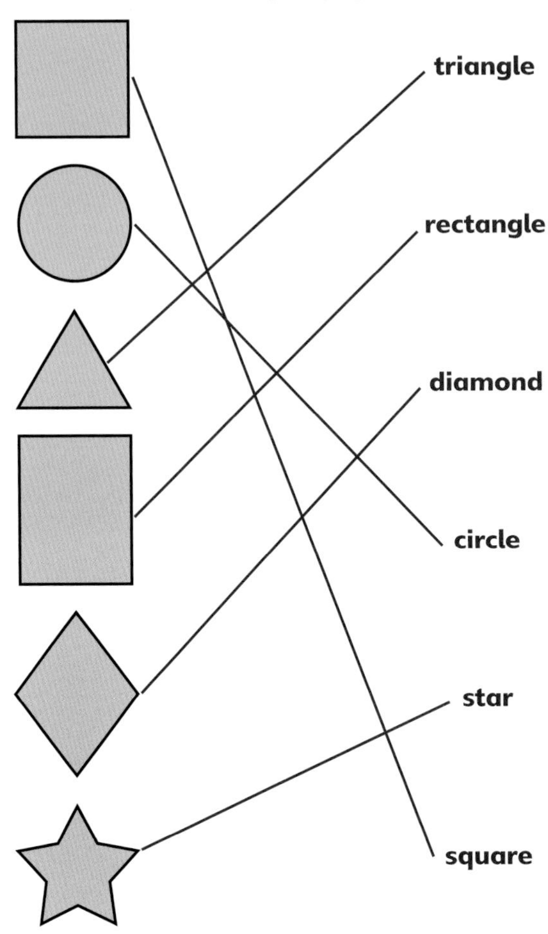

Gilbert's garden paths - page 29
Teacher check

Froggy grids - page 31
Teacher check

Problems bank answers

How many? - page 34

1. 5
2. 8
3. 460p

Bookworm- page 35

1. 16
2. 4

The stairs - page 36

1. 7
2. 4th stair

Mr Snail - CD only

1. 5 days

Who sits where? - page 37

1.

2. Behind Lily (in top left corner)

Time problems - CD only

1. 3 hours
2. 4 pages

Buttons / Balloons - page 38

Buttons: 15
Balloons: 38

25 pence - page 39

Teacher check

Book balance - page 40

Teacher check

What number am I? / Pocket money - page 41

What number am I?: 12
Pocket money: Reece £9, Luke £4

Hungry snails - page 42

On Wednesday there were 24 lettuces left.
On Friday there were 20 lettuces left.
On Saturday there were 18 lettuces left.
On Sunday there were 16 lettuces left.
The rule is: -2.

Baked beans - CD only

1. Add 2
2. Add 3
3. Add one column that is one tin higher

Grid patterns - page 43

Teacher check

Crummy calculator - page 44

Teacher check

Minibeast races – CD only

1. Winning order: first grasshoppers, ladybirds, spiders, flies, beetles
2. Winning order: first Sue Spider, Ben Beetle, Lou Ladybird, Gary Grasshopper, Fred Fly, Wendy Worm